ROOTED
IN
PRAYER

A PERSONAL PRAYER JOURNAL

WITH INSIGHTS BY

BILLY GRAHAM

ROOTED IN PRAYER:
A PERSONAL PRAYER JOURNAL
WITH INSIGHTS BY BILLY GRAHAM

Paperback Edition
©2007, revised 2008 and 2013 Billy Graham Evangelistic Association

BillyGrahamBookstore.org

ISBN: 978-1-59328-397-1

CONTENTS

THINK BACK to your own childhood for a

moment. When you were young, did you talk with your father in a series of carefully memorized sentences? No, of course not. You talked with him freely and openly about everything—and he delighted in that. The same is true with God, your Heavenly Father. He delights in the prayers of His people! Don't worry whether you're eloquent enough; your father didn't turn you away when you spoke baby talk—and neither does God.

—*Billy Graham*

HOW TO USE THIS JOURNAL

This fresh and usable journal is specially designed to help you cultivate a personal prayer plan and keep your prayer life well grounded. Billy Graham's insights on prayer are found throughout, along with other prayer helps.

Start Any Time of the Year

The journal is intended to be flexible to fit your personal pattern and preferences. You can make daily entries or simply jot down insights and prayers any time you want. By noting key things you pray from day to day, you will become more aware of the different ways God may be answering those prayers.

Whether you write something every day or only periodically, remember that it is better to maintain a regular daily prayer time—even if it is short—than waiting for occasional, longer times to pray (see page 19).

Sample journal entry

Jan. 1, 2013
DATE

Dear Lord, both my friend Kelly and my cousin Cameron need to know You personally as Savior and Lord. Please pursue them with Your love, open their hearts to the Gospel, and rescue them.

Conversation Starters

Notice the Scripture verse at the top of every pair of journaling pages. Prayer is conversation with God, and as you read words from the Bible, whether a verse from the journal or from your own daily Bible reading, you can think of them as "conversation openers" between you and God. Let Him first speak to you through His Word, then spend time with Him in prayer. Many days, if you are alert, the Holy Spirit will use a verse you have read to suggest something He wants you to pray.

Special Helps

The journal includes practical advice on praying for people who need Jesus Christ in their lives (page 23). You can find suggestions about praying for your children (page 50), a section to help when praying for leaders (page 81), and encouragement on how to pray God's own prayer request (page 37). There is also an article based on the personal prayer experience of Ruth Graham (page 65).

May God bless you as you faithfully seek Him.

Remember that GOD HELPS us when we pray. ... This is a mystery we will never fully understand this side of Heaven—but it also is a great comfort. The Bible says, *"The Spirit helps us in our weakness. For we do not know what to pray for as we ought, but the Spirit himself intercedes for us with groanings too deep for words"* (Romans 8:26, ESV). ... That *"the Spirit himself intercedes"* indicates that it is actually God pleading, praying, and mourning through us. Thus we become co-laborers with God, actual partners with Him; our lives are lifted from the low plane of selfishness to the high plane of creativeness with God.

—*Billy Graham*

PRAYER

by Billy Graham

God Himself is the power that makes prayer work. Find out how you can pray more effectively and receive the answers to prayer that only God can give.

The men upon whose shoulders rested the initial responsibility of Christianizing the world came to Jesus with one supreme request. They did not say, "Lord, teach us to preach"; "Lord, teach us to do miracles"; or "Lord, teach us to be wise" … but they said, "Lord, teach us to pray."

No one has given more encouragement to praying than did Jesus. The followers of Christ were both encouraged to pray and taught how to pray. They saw constantly the example He set in praying, and they noted the direct relationship between Jesus' unusual ministry and His devout life of prayer.

Jesus considered prayer more important than food, for the Bible says that hours before breakfast, *"In the morning, having risen a long while before daylight, He went out and departed to a solitary place; and there He prayed"* (Mark 1:35).

To the Son of God, prayer was more important than the assembling of great throngs. The Bible says, *"And great multitudes came together to hear, and to be healed by Him of their infirmities. So He Himself often withdrew into the wilderness and prayed"* (Luke 5:15-16).

> It pleases God to relate His work in the world to the prayers of His people.

The precious hours of fellowship with His Heavenly Father meant more to our Savior than sleep, for the Bible says, *"Now it came to pass in those days that He went out to the mountain to pray, and continued all night in prayer to God"* (Luke 6:12).

He prayed at funerals, and the dead were raised. He prayed over the five loaves and two fishes, and a multitude were fed with a little boy's lunch. He prayed, "Not My will, but Yours," and a way was made whereby sinful men and women might approach a holy God.

It pleased God to relate His work in the world to the prayers of His people. Noah prayed, and God handed him a blueprint of the ark of deliverance. Moses prayed, and God delivered the Israelites from Egyptian bondage. Gideon prayed, and the host of a formidable enemy fled in fear before his valiant, prayerful 300.

Daniel prayed, and the mouths of the lions were closed. Elijah prayed, and the fire of God consumed the sacrifice and licked up the water around the altar. David prayed, and he defeated Goliath on the Philistine battleground.

The disciples prayed, and they were filled with the Holy Spirit so that 3,000 were added to the church in one day. Paul prayed, and hundreds of churches were born in Asia Minor and Europe. God does answer prayer.

Avoid Short-Circuiting

Some prayers are answered with a "yes" and some with a "no." But what about unanswered prayer?

Perhaps your prayers have been mingled with doubts. Perhaps you have prayed selfishly. Perhaps you have asked God for things which were not best for you. "I prayed earnestly and nothing happened," many will say in a tone of dismay. "I asked for guidance, and I'm in serious trouble" … "I asked God for a companion, and I have found no one" … "I asked God for a good home, and look at the misery and confusion in our house."

The Bible says that there are specific reasons why prayers are not answered.

It may be that your prayers are not answered because of disobedience. A disobedient son cannot expect to "have his cake and eat it too," as we say. The Bible says, *"If you do not obey the voice of the Lord your God, to observe carefully all His commandments and His statutes which I command you today, … all these curses will come upon you and overtake you"* (Deuteronomy 28:15).

Perhaps your prayers are not answered because of secret sin. David said (and he should know), *"If I regard iniquity in my heart, the Lord will not hear"* (Psalm 66:18). Sin short-circuits the communication system between earth and Heaven, and your praying with an evil heart will not even reach God.

Another reason for prayers not being answered is selfishness or willfulness. The Bible says, *"You ask and do not receive, because you ask amiss, that you may spend it on your pleasures"* (James 4:3). Prayer serves a dual purpose: the blessing of man and the glory of God. If a prayer is prayed willfully for our own benefit but not for God's glory, it's not worthy of being answered. "Not my will, but Yours, be done" (see Luke 22:42) is the spirit of effectual prayer.

Real prayer is not a vain repetition of words uttered in public for religious display. Jesus said, *"And when you pray, you shall not be like the hypocrites. For they love to pray standing in the synagogues and on the corners of the streets, that they may be seen by men. Assuredly, I say to you, they have their reward"* (Matthew 6:5).

Prayer, in the true sense, is not a futile cry of desperation born of fear or frustration. Thousands of people pray only when they are under great stress, or in danger, overcome by uncertainty. I have been in airplanes when an engine died; then people started praying. We have flown through bad thunderstorms when people who may never have thought to pray before were praying all around us. I have talked to soldiers who told me that they never prayed until they were in the midst of battle. There seems to be an instinct in people to pray in times of trouble.

We know "there are no atheists in foxholes," but the kind of Christianity that fails to reach into our everyday lives will never change the world.

Prayer is not limited to conventional religious postures; nor is it restricted to houses of worship or religious ceremony. The Bible says, *"I desire therefore that the men pray everywhere, lifting up holy hands, without wrath and doubting"* (I Timothy 2:8).

> Very few of us have learned how to fully develop the power of prayer.

When you pray, your physical posture is not so important as the attitude of your heart. Many people put a great deal of emphasis on the position of the body during prayer. Some groups or sects insist that you kneel every time you pray or that you fold your hands in a certain way. All of this is relatively unimportant, though kneeling is an act of humility when sincerely done.

Pray in Step With God

Praying is simply a two-way conversation between you and God. The reason many of the great saints have closed their eyes while praying is to shut out the affairs of the world so that their minds could be completely concentrated on their conversations with God. However, nowhere in Scripture does it say that even the closing of the eyes is important, though it certainly lends itself to the attitude of prayer.

The next question many ask is: "Who is told to pray?" Scripture gives the answer, "All men."

Again, many ask: "Where are we commanded to pray?" Paul gives us the answer when he says, "Everywhere."

Some may also ask, "When are we told to pray?" The Scripture says, "Always." It is a command, a duty, and a privilege. In this modern age in which we live, we have learned to harness the power of the mighty Niagara and turn its force to our use and our good. We have learned to hold steam captive in boilers and release its tremendous power to turn our machines. We have learned how to contain gasoline vapors in a cylinder and explode them at the appointed second to move our automobiles and trucks quickly along our highways. We have even discovered the secret of releasing energy in the atom, which is capable of destroying entire cities and civilizations.

> God Himself is the power that makes prayer work.

But very few of us have learned how to fully develop the power of prayer. We have not yet learned that men and women are more powerful when they are in prayer than when they are behind the most powerful guns we have ever developed. We have not learned that a nation is more powerful when it unites in earnest prayer than when its resources are channeled into defensive weapons. We have not discovered that the answers to all our problems can be had through contact with Almighty God.

Scores of missionaries, in all parts of the world, have told me, "Please get the people back home to pray for us. We would rather have their prayers than anything else." If the Christians back home realized how much their prayers meant to these valiant heroes of the faith, they would not cease to pray day and night for their representatives out there in foreign mission fields.

Christian workers here at home also need your prayers. I know from personal experience. We are only able to move forward in our evangelistic work—the Crusades, the film ministry, television, radio, and Internet—by your prayers. If it were not for the prayers of thousands of God's people throughout the world, our ministry would completely fail.

Approach the Throne of God

Now let us look at prayer objectively. What does the Bible say about effectual praying?

First: Prayer is for God's children.

Jesus said, *"When you pray, say: 'Our Father ...'"* (Luke 11:2).

God has a particular responsibility to His children; and unless we have been born into the family of God through the new birth, we have no right to ask favors of God. The Bible says, *"But as many as received Him, to them He gave the right to become children of God, to those who believe in His name"* (John 1:12).

I have had new Christians say to me, "I don't know how to pray. I don't have the right words."

When our children were just learning to talk and had difficulty finding the right words, they still managed to make themselves understood to my wife and me, and the mistakes they made only endeared them to us. In fact, I am sure I treasure their early attempts at conversation more than the words of most adults speaking without hesitation and without error.

My friend, if your prayers have not been answered, God invites you to the intimacy of spiritual sonship, *"that you may become blameless and harmless, children of God without fault in the midst of a crooked and perverse generation, among whom you shine as lights in the world"* (Philippians 2:15).

Second: Effectual prayer is offered in faith.

The Bible says, *"Therefore I say to you, whatever things you ask when you pray, believe that you receive them, and you will have them"* (Mark 11:24).

Maltbie Babcock said, "Our prayers are to mean something to us if they are to mean anything to God." It goes without saying that if our prayers are aimless, meaningless, and mingled with doubt, they will go unanswered. Prayer is more than a wish turned heavenward … it is the voice of faith directed Godward.

Third: Dynamic prayer emanates from an obedient heart.

> Obedience is the master key to effectual prayer.

The Bible says, *"And whatever we ask we receive from Him, because we keep His commandments and do those things that are pleasing in His sight"* (1 John 3:22).

I know a wealthy father who refused to get his son a bicycle because the boy's report card showed disgracefully low marks, a yard remained unraked, and other assignments had not been carried out. I am sure the father would not have been wise to lavish gifts upon such a disobedient and ungrateful son.

The Bible says, *"However, if you do not obey the voice of the Lord, but rebel against the commandment of the Lord, then the hand of the Lord will be against you"* (1 Samuel 12:15).

If you want to get your prayers through to God, surrender your stubborn will to Him, and He will hear your cry. Obedience is the master key to effectual prayer.

Fourth: We are to pray in Christ's Name.

Jesus said, *"And whatever you ask in My name, that I will do, that the Father may be glorified in the Son"* (John 14:13).

We are not worthy to approach the holy throne of God except through our Advocate, Jesus Christ.

The Bible says, *"Seeing then that we have a great High Priest who has passed through the heavens, Jesus the Son of God … let us therefore come boldly to the throne of grace"* (Hebrews 4:14, 16).

God, for Christ's sake, forgives our sins. God, for Christ's sake, supplies our needs. God, for Christ's sake, receives our prayers. The person who comes with confidence to the throne of grace has seen that his approach to God has been made possible because of Jesus Christ.

Many may ask, "Is there no other way to pray except through Jesus Christ?" You may pray, but according to the Bible, *"there is … one Mediator between God and men, the Man Christ Jesus"* (1 Timothy 2:5).

Fifth: We must desire the will of God.

Even our Lord, contrary to His own disposition at the moment, said, *"O My Father, if this cup cannot pass away from Me unless I drink it, Your will be done"* (Matthew 26:42).

Prayer couples you with God's true purposes for you and the world. It not only brings the blessings of God's will to your own personal life, but it brings you the added blessing of being in step with God's plan.

And last: Our prayer must be for God's glory.

The model prayer which Jesus has given us concludes with, *"Yours is the kingdom and the power and the glory forever"* (Matthew 6:13). If we are to have our prayers answered, we must give God the glory. Our Lord said to His disciples, *"And whatever you ask in My name, that I will do, that the Father may be glorified in the Son"* (John 14:13).

What a privilege is ours: the privilege of prayer! Christian, examine your heart, reconsecrate your life, yield yourself to God unreservedly, for only those who pray through a clean heart will be heard by Him. The Bible says, *"The effective, fervent prayer of a righteous man avails much"* (James 5:16).

We are to pray in times of adversity, lest we become faithless and unbelieving. We are to pray in times of prosperity, lest we become boastful and proud.

We are to pray in times of danger, lest we become fearful and doubting. We need to pray in times of security, lest we become self-sufficient. Sinners, pray to a merciful God for forgiveness! Christians, pray for an outpouring of God's Spirit upon a willful, evil, unrepentant world. Parents, pray that God may crown your home with grace and mercy! Children, pray for the salvation of your parents!

Christians, saints of God, pray that the dew of Heaven may fall on earth's dry, thirsty ground, and that righteousness may cover the earth as the waters cover the sea. Pray, believing, with this promise of our Savior in mind, *"Whatever things you ask when you pray, believe that you receive them, and you will have them"* (Mark 11:24).

"Satan trembles when he sees the weakest saint upon his knees"—so pray, Christian, pray!

REJOICE IN THE LORD ALWAYS. ...

Let your gentleness be known to all. ... In everything by prayer and
supplication, with thanksgiving, let your requests be made known to
God; and the peace of God, which surpasses all understanding,
will guard your hearts and minds through Christ Jesus.

—Philippians 4:4–7

DATE 11.28.15

Lord, I pray that the relationship
between me and Christopher ear is mended! I
have been the cause of strife, taking to
anger rather than teaching him. Please rid me
of that. That is not of you. I want to
produce the Fruit of the Spirit in him, not
that of this world. He is such a lovely
person, and I have never met anyone with
a more pure heart. He's so much like
Christ. He just needs to be taught, not
scolded. Help me, Lord. Help me!

DATE 12.14.15

Father, thank you for the relationships
that you have given us here on earth.
While we know that there is no love
greater than the one you have for us,
you have recognized our desire for
companionship and physical touch. So
thank you for letting others fill that
for us, no matter how short the
season may be. You know the desires
of my heart and those of my children,
Lord. Please help us with this feeling
of lack. I love you, forever and ever. Amen!

How to Use This Journal, see page 5

Happy is the man who has learned the secret of coming to God in daily prayer. Even 15 minutes alone with God every morning before you start the day can change circumstances and remove mountains!

—*Billy Graham*

Now it came to pass, as He was praying in a certain place, when He ceased, that one of His disciples said to Him,

"LORD, TEACH US TO PRAY ... ."

So He said to them, "When you pray, say: 'Our Father in heaven, hallowed be Your name. Your kingdom come.'"

—*Luke 11:1-2*

DATE

DATE

When uncertain you are praying the right thing, see page 6 or 21

The men upon whose shoulders rested the initial responsibility of Christianizing the world came to Jesus with one supreme request. They did not say, "Lord, teach us to preach"; "Lord, teach us to do miracles"; or "Lord, teach us to be wise" … but they said, "Lord, teach us to pray."

—*Billy Graham*

For he says to Moses, "I WILL HAVE MERCY on whom I have mercy, and I will have compassion on whom I have compassion." So then it depends not on human will or exertion, but on God, who has mercy.

—Romans 9:15–16, ESV

DATE

DATE

Perhaps you do not know how to pray. Why don't you start now by saying, "God, be merciful to me, a sinner"? That simple, direct prayer, sincerely said, will open new horizons of spiritual victory for you and add a new dimension to your life.

—Billy Graham

Practical Advice From Billy Graham

Set aside time each day to spend with God. It may be early in the morning, or at least before you begin the day's regular activities. Make it a time when you are mentally alert, when you have no distractions and you are not rushed. Discipline yourself to keep this time every day, even when travel or a busy schedule makes it difficult. Make it such a regular part of your life that you would no more skip it than you would miss eating a meal.

"See, O Lord, that I AM IN DISTRESS; my soul is troubled; my heart is overturned within me. ... The Lord is my portion," says my soul, "Therefore I hope in Him!" The Lord is good to those who wait for Him, to the soul who seeks Him. It is good that one should hope and wait quietly for the salvation of the Lord.

—*Lamentations 1:20; 3:24-26*

DATE _____ ,

_____

_____

_____

_____

_____

_____

_____

_____

DATE _____

_____

_____

_____

_____

_____

_____

_____

_____

_____

God even hears our prayers when we can't quite put them
into words—times, for example, when our hearts are too
burdened or confused even to speak. The Bible says,
*"The Spirit helps us in our weakness. For we do not know what to
pray for as we ought, but the Spirit himself intercedes for us with
groanings too deep for words"* (Romans 8:26, ESV).

—Billy Graham

Almost EVERY WEEK, I get at least one letter from someone who has prayed for a loved one for many years without any apparent effect. And yet they go on to say that their prayers finally have been answered. In other words, if God has put a burden on your heart for an unbelieving loved one, keep on praying for her. Remember: You may be the only person on earth who is still praying for that person—and that is an awesome responsibility.

—*Billy Graham*

HOW TO PRAY FOR LOST PEOPLE

by Billy Graham

As Christians, we often pray for the sick, for each other, for the nation, and many regularly pray for "the lost," but we should also pray by name for specific lost people. In the familiar parable Jesus told about the lost sheep (see Luke 15), the shepherd did not go out to see if he could find just any stray sheep he might come across. He went searching for a particular sheep. Pray that way, for specific lost people.

We may pray that a person will find God, but Jesus said it the other way around—He said that He came *"to seek and to save the lost"* (Luke 19:10, ESV). Jesus does the seeking, and the Holy Spirit opens a person's heart. That's what we should be praying for. The first convert to Christ in Europe, that we know about, was a businesswoman in Ephesus named Lydia, a dealer in fine fabric. The Bible says God *"opened her heart to respond to the things spoken"* (Acts 16:14, NASB). There is no other way to get an unsaved person to respond. It took me years to understand this. We may pray for the preaching and pray for someone to turn to God, but the preaching will have little effect and the person will not make a decision to turn without the Holy Spirit.

Make a list of people you know who need Jesus Christ in their lives, and pray for them, not once or twice, but persistently. When we pray urgently and faithfully by name for lost people we truly care about, asking God to reach them, God works—often in unique and unexpected ways—to open hearts to Himself.

Start With People You Know

Look around and identify friends, neighbors, co-workers, fellow students, and family who do not know Jesus Christ as their Savior. Write their names here; pray for them often.

1 _____

2 _____

3 _____

4 _____

5 _____

6 _____

7 _____

8 _____

9 _____

10 _____

Because he has set **HIS LOVE** upon Me,
therefore I will deliver him; I will set him
on high, because he has known My name.
He shall call upon Me, and I will answer him.

—Psalm 91:14-15

DATE

DATE

Praying for someone you don't know, see page 41

Prayer is simply talking to God—and the most important thing
I can say about this is that God wants you to talk to Him!
—*Billy Graham*

This Book of the LAW shall not depart from your mouth, but you shall meditate in it day and night, that you may observe to do according to all that is written in it. For then you will make your way prosperous, and then you will have good success.

—*Joshua 1:8*

DATE

DATE

To Encourage You in Prayer

Desire the Will of God

Jesus taught us to pray, "Your will be done." The key is not the words, but your attitude. Seek God's will and God's best for whatever you are praying about. He may respond in unexpected ways that please Him and will delight you. *"Your will be done on earth as it is in heaven"* (Matthew 6:10).

Prayer and Bible study are inseparably linked. Effective prayer is
born out of the prompting of God's Spirit as we read His Word.
—*Billy Graham*

Now therefore, our God, HEAR THE PRAYER
of Your servant, and his supplications. ... We do not present
our supplications before You because of our righteous deeds,
but because of Your great mercies. O Lord, hear! O Lord, forgive!
O Lord, listen and act! Do not delay for Your own sake, my God.

—Daniel 9:17-19

DATE

DATE

Praying for our leaders, see pages 81-83

When you pray, pray! Too often we use petty little
petitions, oratorical exercises, or the words of others
rather than the cries of our inmost being.
—*Billy Graham*

HEAR INSTRUCTION and be

wise, and do not disdain it. Blessed is the man who
listens to me, watching daily at my gates,
waiting at the posts of my doors.

—Proverbs 8:33-34

DATE

DATE

What pleases God, see page 121

The soul demands as much attention as the body.
It needs fellowship and communion with God. It needs worship,
quietness, and meditation. Unless the soul is fed and exercised daily,
it becomes weak and shriveled, discontented, confused, restless.
—*Billy Graham*

If you then, being evil, know how to give **GOOD GIFTS**
to your children, how much more will your
Father who is in heaven give good
things to those who ask Him!

—Matthew 7:11

DATE

DATE

Creative Prayer Suggestion

Make a "prayer book" of pictures. This would work well for family, leaders, and missionaries. Often, seeing people gives us a personal burden as we pray for them.

So often we are inclined to think that the only answer God
can give our prayers is "yes." We need to remember that "no" is an
answer also. … God does not always give us what we want; He gives us
what we need. Just as a good parent does not grant all the requests of
his child, God does not answer every request in the way we desire.

—*Billy Graham*

Do not fear; ... let not your hands be weak.
The Lord your God in your midst, the Mighty One, will save;
HE WILL REJOICE OVER YOU WITH GLADNESS,
He will quiet you with His love, He will rejoice over you with singing.
—Zephaniah 3:16-17

DATE _____

_____

_____

_____

_____

_____

_____

_____

_____

_____

DATE _____

_____

_____

_____

_____

_____

_____

_____

_____

_____

_____

God wants us to talk with Him, our Heavenly Father, and
He takes delight in us when we come to Him in prayer.
—*Billy Graham*

It pleases God to relate HIS WORK in the world to the prayers of His people. Noah prayed, and God handed him a blueprint of the ark of deliverance. Moses prayed, and God delivered the Israelites from Egyptian bondage. Gideon prayed, and the host of a formidable enemy fled in fear before his valiant, prayerful 300. Daniel prayed, and the mouths of the lions were closed. Elijah prayed, and the fire of God consumed the sacrifice and licked up the water around the altar. David prayed, and he defeated Goliath on the Philistine battleground. The disciples prayed, and they were filled with the Holy Spirit so that 3,000 were added to the church in one day. Paul prayed, and hundreds of churches were born in Asia Minor and Europe. God does answer prayer.

—*Billy Graham*

GOD'S OWN PRAYER REQUEST

"Ask of me, and I will make the nations your heritage."
—*Psalm 2:8, ESV*

Some refer to this verse as God's own prayer request. He wants every nation to turn to Him. Join me in continuing to ask Him.

—*Billy Graham*

What God Wants

While praying for our own requests, do we give time to praying what God has requested? The Father's plan is to give the nations to the Son (see Psalm 2:7-8). As children of the Father and co-heirs with Christ (see Romans 8:17), we each have a stake in this plan. God is passionate about the people of all nations, and it is the Father's request that we ask for the nations. He gives us the responsibility of asking. Martin Luther said, "Prayer is not overcoming God's reluctance, but laying hold of His willingness." Through prayer, you can take direct action to bring the Gospel to the people of the world.

Praying for the Nations

There are many ways to pray for the world. You can use a globe or map to pray for a nation a week (or find a list of world nations on the Internet). You can focus on countries where you feel a connection, such as a country you have visited that needs the Gospel, countries where your church has a missionary, or a country that God has placed on your heart. You can also focus on nations where there are few Christians (look up *unreached peoples* or *unreached nations* on the Internet).

Praying God's Request

When praying for the nations, you may wish to pray based on words of Scripture:

> *"All the ends of the earth shall remember*
> *and turn to the Lord,*
> *and all the families of the nations*
> *shall worship before you.*
> *For kingship belongs to the Lord,*
> *and he rules over the nations"* (Psalm 22:27-28, ESV).

> *"Thus it is written, ... that repentance and forgiveness of sins*
> *should be proclaimed in his name to all nations"* (Luke 24:46-47, ESV).

O God, You are my God; early will I seek You;

MY SOUL THIRSTS FOR YOU;

my flesh longs for You in a dry and thirsty
land where there is no water.

—Psalm 63:1

DATE

DATE

Prayers that outlast you, see page 64

DATE

God says that only those who hunger and thirst after
righteousness will receive it. God thrusts this heavenly
manna on no one. You must desire it above everything else.
Your yearning for God must supersede all other desires. It
must be like a gnawing hunger and a burning thirst.
—*Billy Graham*

And so, from the day we heard,

WE HAVE NOT CEASED TO PRAY FOR YOU,

asking that you may be filled with the knowledge of his will in all
spiritual wisdom and understanding, so as to walk in a manner worthy
of the Lord, fully pleasing to him, bearing fruit in every good work
and increasing in the knowledge of God.

—*Colossians 1:9-10, ESV*

DATE

_____
_____
_____
_____
_____
_____
_____
_____
_____
_____
_____
_____
_____

DATE

_____
_____
_____
_____
_____
_____
_____

Practical Advice From Billy Graham

Come with a spirit of expectancy and obedience. Expect God to meet you
through His Word, and tell Him that you want to be taught by Him. Come
with a willingness to hear His Word and then to obey it. Remember: God
the Holy Spirit has inspired the Bible, and we must look expectantly to
Him to illumine our understanding of it.

It's easier to pray for someone we know rather than
someone we don't know. But has it ever occurred to you that
those you know the least may need your prayers the most?
Don't let the fact that you don't know someone
keep you from praying for them.
—*Billy Graham*

YOUR WORDS were found, and I ate them,
and Your word was to me the joy and rejoicing of
my heart; for I am called by Your name,
O Lord God of hosts.

—Jeremiah 15:16

DATE

DATE

Praying for your children, see pages 50-51

Prayer by itself is like a diet without protein!
Yes, prayer is important to our spiritual growth—but of
even greater importance is God's Word, the Bible.
—*Billy Graham*

43

For **WE DO NOT KNOW** what we should pray for as we ought, but the Spirit Himself makes intercession for us with groanings which cannot be uttered. Now He who searches the hearts knows what the mind of the Spirit is, because He makes intercession for the saints according to the will of God.

—Romans 8:26-27

DATE

DATE

An attitude that is key to prayer, see page 26

Pray and ask God to guide you. … Often, we try to tell God
what we want Him to do—but ask Him to help you guard
against this and to seek His will instead of your own.
—*Billy Graham*

[Daniel] knelt down on his knees **THREE TIMES** that day, and prayed and gave thanks before his God, as was his custom since early days.

—*Daniel 6:10*

DATE

_____

_____

_____

_____

_____

_____

_____

_____

_____

_____

_____

_____

_____

_____

DATE

_____

_____

_____

_____

_____

_____

_____

_____

_____

_____

_____

The three most important things you can do are, number one, pray ... number two, pray ... number three, pray.
—*Billy Graham*

To Encourage You in Prayer

Search Your Heart

God may not respond when you allow sin to remain in your life. If so, don't stop praying. Rather, confess your sins or wrong motives to God. He already knows your heart. God has promised always to respond to that prayer (see 1 John 1:9). *"If I had cherished iniquity in my heart, the Lord would not have listened"* (Psalm 66:18, ESV).

And my God shall supply
ALL YOUR NEED
according to His riches in
glory by Christ Jesus.

—*Philippians 4:19*

DATE

DATE

Praying for the leaders in your church, see page 99

God not only cares about our needs, but He is also delighted
when we bring them to Him in prayer. Jesus said, *"If you ... know
how to give good gifts to your children, how much more will your Father
who is in heaven give good things to those who ask Him!"* (Matthew 7:11).
—*Billy Graham*

HOW TO PRAY SCRIPTURE
FOR YOUR CHILDREN

"The word of God is living and active."
—*Hebrews 4:12, ESV*

One of the most powerful ways to pray for children is to use Scripture. Because the Bible is the living Word of God, you can pray His Word back to Him, interceding for your children and grandchildren about the very things that matter to God.

Pray for Things Mentioned in a Verse:

Luke 2:52 *"Jesus increased in wisdom and stature, and in favor with God and men."*

Pray for the child by name, asking that he or she will increase in wisdom (the mind), in stature (physically), in favor with God (spiritual), and in favor with man (social).

Focus on God's Desires:

Matthew 18:14 *"It is not the will of your Father who is in heaven that one of these little ones should perish."*

Pray for your child's salvation based on God's will for the child (see also 1 Timothy 2:4; 2 Peter 3:9; 3 John 1:4).

Insert Children's Names Into a Verse:

Psalm 91:11, ESV *"He will command his angels concerning [names] to guard [them] in all [their] ways."*

OTHER SCRIPTURE TO PRAY FOR YOUR CHILDREN:

- Father, give us understanding and wisdom in bringing up our children.
  Proverbs 2:6

- May they be taught by the Lord and experience peace.
  Isaiah 54:13

- That the power of the Gospel may change and fill their lives.
  Romans 1:16

- May they be swift to hear, slow to speak, and slow to anger.
  James 1:19

- May they learn to be content with what they have.
  Hebrews 13:5

- May they not forget to do what is right and to share.
  Hebrews 13:16

- That they grow in wisdom and in the knowledge of God.
  Colossians 1:9-12

- May they abound more and more in how they please You.
  1 Thessalonians 4:1

- That they submit to their elders and show humility to one another.
  1 Peter 5:5

- Provide them peaceful sleep, and safety day and night.
  Psalm 4:8

- Rescue them from evil attacks and preserve them in their faith.
  2 Timothy 4:18

- Enable them to be doers of the Word and not hearers only.
  James 1:22

- That they would learn to effectively share their faith.
  Philemon 1:6

I know how to be abased, and I know how
to abound. Everywhere and in all things
I HAVE LEARNED BOTH
to be full and to be hungry, both
to abound and to suffer need.

—Philippians 4:12

DATE
_____
_____
_____
_____
_____
_____
_____
_____
_____

DATE
_____
_____
_____
_____
_____
_____
_____
_____
_____

DATE

Remember: There is a difference between our needs
and our wants. We may want something for ourselves, but it
might not be something we really need. When we honestly
need something (and don't simply want it), God tells us to
bring it to Him and trust Him for the outcome.

—*Billy Graham*

And [Moses] said, "Please, show me Your
glory." ... Now the Lord descended in the cloud
and STOOD WITH HIM THERE, and
proclaimed the name of the Lord. And the Lord passed before him
and proclaimed, "The Lord, the Lord God, merciful and gracious,
longsuffering, and abounding in goodness and truth ... ."

—*Exodus 33:18; 34:5-6*

DATE

DATE

Creative Prayer Suggestion

Make a list of needy people in your church or neighborhood. Pray for
them with your family, and explore ways that various family members can
reach out to them.

How can you keep your mind from wandering when you pray?
Remember what you are doing: talking to God. If you had an
opportunity to talk with the president, I doubt if your mind would
wander. But you and I have the privilege of talking to someone
far greater: the King of kings and the Lord of lords!
—*Billy Graham*

O Lord, I have heard Your speech and was afraid;
O Lord, **REVIVE YOUR WORK** in the
midst of the years! In the midst of the years make it known;
in wrath remember mercy. God came. ... His glory covered
the heavens, and the earth was full of His praise.

—Habakkuk 3:2-3

DATE

DATE

    What God wants, see page 25

Who knows what God might do if His people began to pray fervently for spiritual revival? Perhaps one reason Satan has gained such a hold on so many lives is because we don't pray enough. Our prayer should be that of the Prophet Habakkuk: *"O Lord, I have heard Your speech and was afraid; O Lord, revive Your work in the midst of the years! In the midst of the years make it known; in wrath remember mercy"* (Habakkuk 3:2, NKJV).
—*Billy Graham*

THE EYES OF YOUR UNDERSTANDING

being enlightened; that you may know what is the hope of His calling, what are the riches of the glory of His inheritance in the saints, and what is the exceeding greatness of His power toward us who believe, according to the working of His mighty power which He worked in Christ when He raised Him from the dead and seated Him at His right hand in the heavenly places.

—Ephesians 1:18-20

DATE

DATE

Encouragement for your prayers, see page 92

The Bible says God *"is able to do far more abundantly
than all that we ask or think, according to the power at work within us"*
(Ephesians 3:20, ESV). One of the ways His power is at work in
us is through the prayers of His people, and that's one reason
why we should always pray when we face hard times.
—*Billy Graham*

Therefore, AS THE ELECT OF GOD, holy and beloved, put on tender mercies, kindness, humility, meekness, longsuffering; bearing with one another, and forgiving one another, if anyone has a complaint against another; even as Christ forgave you, so you also must do.

—*Colossians 3:12–13*

DATE

DATE

The most eloquent prayer is the prayer through hands that heal and bless.
—*Billy Graham*

Practical Advice From Billy Graham

Read through the Bible systematically. It is far too easy to dwell only on familiar passages or skip around almost at random finding passages that happen to appeal to us. But we need to understand *"the whole counsel of God"* (Acts 20:27), and we need therefore to read and study every part of the Bible. Some people find it helpful to have a plan by which they will cover the entire Bible in a year.

Thus says the Lord ... "CALL TO ME,
and I will answer you, and show you great
and mighty things, which you do not know."

—*Jeremiah 33:2-3*

DATE

DATE

"Yes" is not the only answer, see page 33

A mystery and wonder of prayer is that God often
waits until someone asks. I once heard it said that Heaven's
storeroom is full of answers for which no one bothered to ask.

—*Billy Graham*

I firmly believe God continues to

ANSWER THE PRAYERS

of His people even after He has taken them to Heaven.
Never forget that God isn't bound by time the way we are.
We see only the present moment; God sees everything.
We see only part of what He is doing; He sees it all. Long
after you and I are gone, God will still be at work—and
many of the things we prayed for will finally come to pass.

—*Billy Graham*

A POWERFUL WAY TO PRAY GOD'S WORD

by Robert J. Morgan

Many years ago several young college students sat around the old oak table in Ruth Bell Graham's kitchen, listening to her stories. We were lonely and homesick. College life had been rougher than expected. Ruth's eyes glowed as she told us of her own bouts with loneliness, particularly of an unsparing incident that once laid her low.

"When I was 13," she said, "my parents, missionaries in China, enrolled me in boarding school in what is now Pyongyang, North Korea. It was a difficult parting, and on my last night home, I earnestly prayed that I would die." Ruth didn't die, but arriving in Korea, she reeled under pounding waves of homesickness. Every night, she buried her head in her pillow and cried herself to sleep. Finally in desperation, she went to her sister, Rosa, also enrolled in Pyongyang.

> What Ruth Graham taught me about prayer

"I don't know what to tell you to do," Rosa replied bluntly, "unless you take some verse and put your own name in it. See if that helps." Ruth picked up her Bible and turned to a favorite chapter, Isaiah 53, and put her name in it: "He was pierced for Ruth's transgressions, he was crushed for my iniquities; the punishment that brought Ruth peace was upon him, and by his wounds I am healed" (v. 5).

"I claimed that verse and knew then," Ruth told us, "that I would make it."

Cure for a Knotted Stomach

I have often remembered Mrs. Graham's words, and have developed a variation of that technique. For several years now, I've devoted a portion of my daily prayer time to taking various passages of Scripture and putting my name in them—or the names of others. I record these prayers in a journal as petitions to the Lord.

> God loves to be reminded of His promises.

"God loves to be reminded of His promises," Ruth went on to tell us on that autumn evening in 1971. "He never rebukes us for asking too much."

Worriers like me must frequently remember that. We often suffer knotted stomachs, pounding heads, and spastic colons, when our real need is bent knees. James 5:16 teaches that the prayers of a righteous person are *"powerful and effective."* They can keep us and our loved ones from danger, spare us from evil, instill us with wisdom, and nudge us toward God.

> He never rebukes us for asking too much.

But what exactly should we pray? Romans 8:26 warns that sometimes we *"do not know what we ought to pray for."* But when we pray using the words of Scripture, we can be confident of praying acceptably before God.

For example, I found a passage in Ephesians 4 that I adapted for my daughter Hannah. I wrote it in my prayer notebook, then offered it aloud to the Lord: Dear Lord, I pray today for Hannah, that You will help her avoid unwholesome talk, and teach her to speak only what is helpful in building others up according to their needs. Keep her from grieving Your Holy Spirit.

Concerned for a struggling young friend, I prayed for him along the lines of Luke 11:1 and Hebrews 4:16—Heavenly Father, teach James to pray. May he learn to approach Your throne of grace with confidence so that he can receive mercy and find grace to help him in his time of need.

In praying for my missionary friend in the Ivory Coast of West Africa, I've leaned on Ephesians 6:19: God, I pray whenever Clint opens his mouth, words may be given him so that he will fearlessly make known the mystery of the Gospel.

And praying for my church, I have sometimes taken my cue from the Lord Jesus in John 17:23—Father, may we be brought to complete unity to let the world know that You sent us and have loved us.

Habits Worth Forming

Keeping a prayer journal helps keep my habits on track, but those uncomfortable keeping a notebook can use the margins of their Bibles for the same purposes. As meaningful verses are found, they can be switched into prayers and offered aloud. A record of the person prayed for and the date can be jotted alongside the text with a fine-point pen.

Another version of this technique involves memorized Scripture. When retiring at night or while driving down the highway, reflect on a beloved verse and transform it into a prayer. Just the other day, after having said exactly the wrong thing to someone, I drove off while earnestly praying Psalm 141:3—*"Set a guard over my mouth, O Lord; keep watch over the door of my lips."*

This habit can also be extended to the hymnbook. Want to pray a special prayer for your mother? Adapt Frances Ridley Havergal's famous hymn to say: "Take Mom's life and let it be/Consecrated, Lord, to Thee;/Take her moments and her days—/Let them flow in ceaseless praise." Instead of listening to the radio, use your drive time to pray for family and friends by singing your way down the highway, punching their names into the stanzas.

A Remarkable Prayer Time

Some time ago, my wife and I took in a troubled young man with a long history of drug and alcohol abuse. We loved him dearly and beamed at his progress. But after several months of sobriety, he suddenly relapsed into a vicious world of beer and cocaine.

The next six months were a nightmare, but he eventually consented to let us enroll him in a drug rehab program. He entered just before his birthday and I told him that in lieu of a present, I would pray for him for an hour when the day came.

When his birthday arrived, I wondered how I could pray so long for one person. Late in the evening after everyone else was in bed, I slipped to the living room and knelt by the sofa.

> When we pray using words of Scripture, we can be confident of praying acceptably before God.

I opened my Bible to Genesis and thumbed through page after page. Before me were well-worn chapters, underlined verses, highlighted passages. One-by-one I adapted them into prayers for Mark.

I have seldom felt such power in prayer, and the hour went quickly. I ran out of time long before running out of verses. Meanwhile in the rehab center, Mark turned the corner. That was seven years ago, and he is still doing great. We can trace his turn-around to the very week of his birthday.

If you find your stomach knotting, your head pounding, and your teeth clenched, discover the simple remedy of bending your knees. Remember the advice that pulled Ruth Graham from depression. Find a portion of Scripture, and put a name in it.

My brethren, COUNT IT ALL JOY when you fall
into various trials, knowing that the testing of your faith
produces patience. But let patience have its perfect work,
that you may be perfect and complete, lacking nothing.

—*James 1:2-4*

DATE

DATE

Praying when your life hits bottom, see page 65

All the masterpieces of art contain both light and shadow.
A happy life is not one filled with only sunshine, but one
which uses both light and shadow to produce beauty.
—*Billy Graham*

If you **ABIDE IN ME,** and My words abide in you,
you will ask what you desire, and it shall be done for you.
By this My Father is glorified, that you bear much fruit;
so you will be My disciples.
—*John 15:7-8*

DATE

DATE

Prayer is not our using of God; it more often puts
us in a position where God can use us.
—*Billy Graham*

To Encourage You in Prayer

Pray in Faith

Express your requests freely to God in childlike faith. As a child who trusts a wise and loving parent, ask in complete faith that He is able to do whatever you ask and that He will know what is best.

"The effective, fervent prayer of a righteous man avails much. Elijah was a man with a nature like ours, and he prayed earnestly that it would not rain; and it did not rain on the land for three years and six months. And he prayed again, and the heaven gave rain, and the earth produced its fruit" (James 5:16-18).

DATE

DATE

Not lagging in diligence, fervent in spirit, serving the Lord;
rejoicing in hope, patient in tribulation, continuing

STEADFASTLY IN PRAYER ...

—*Romans 12:11–12*

DATE

DATE

Praying for one who hurts you, see page 115

We are to pray in times of adversity, lest we become faithless
and unbelieving. We are to pray in times of prosperity,
lest we become boastful and proud. We are to pray in times of
danger, lest we become fearful and doubting. We need to
pray in times of security, lest we become self-sufficient.
—*Billy Graham*

... That He would grant you, according to the

RICHES OF HIS GLORY,

to be strengthened with might through His Spirit in the inner man,
that Christ may dwell in your hearts through faith; that you, being
rooted and grounded in love, may be able to comprehend with all
the saints what is the width and length and depth and height ...

—Ephesians 3:16-18

DATE

DATE

Praying for our nation's leaders, see pages 81-83

You cannot afford to be too busy to pray.
A prayerless Christian is a powerless Christian.

—*Billy Graham*

But Jesus answered them,
"MY FATHER HAS BEEN WORKING
until now, and I have been working."
—John 5:17

DATE

DATE

Creative Prayer Suggestion

When praying for the nation and the world, pray about the front-page events of your local newspaper.

When we think of "unanswered" prayer, it may be
that we do not understand the way in which God responds to our
requests. ... Sometimes our prayers are answered in a way that we fail
to recognize. ... If your prayers are not always answered as you expect,
it is not because God is not working in the situation.
—*Billy Graham*

I have called upon You, for YOU WILL HEAR ME, O God; incline Your ear to me, and hear my speech. Show Your marvelous lovingkindness by Your right hand, O You who save those who trust in You from those who rise up against them. Keep me as the apple of Your eye; hide me under the shadow of Your wings.

—Psalm 17:6-8

DATE

DATE

Prayer from a broken heart, see page 119

My time spent in prayer with You, dear Lord, is the highlight of my day. To know You are waiting to have this communion humbles me. Yet You say I can come boldly—this I do now, knowing You hear me!
—*Billy Graham*

Pray for our WORLD and its LEADERS every day—
beginning now. Yes, you may wonder exactly what good
prayers like this are accomplishing because our world has so
many problems—and they never seem to get any better.
But listen: Have you ever asked yourself how much worse off
the world might be if God's people didn't pray?
Only in eternity will we know the full impact of our prayers.

—Billy Graham

HOW TO PRAY FOR OUR LEADERS

What the Bible says:

> "First of all, then, I urge that *supplications*, *prayers*, *intercessions*, and *thanksgivings* be made for all people, for kings and all who are in high positions, that we may lead a peaceful and quiet life, godly and dignified in every way. This is good, and it is pleasing in the sight of God our Savior."
>
> —*1 Timothy 2:1-3, ESV*

- Supplication (or *petition*) is simply asking. God urges us to ask, and He is pleased when we do.

- Prayer is talking to God, anywhere, anytime.

- Intercession is praying for someone else. The Bible tells us that Jesus Christ constantly intercedes for us (see Romans 8:34), so it pleases God when we intercede for someone else—including heads of state and others in authority—because we are doing what Christ does.

- Thanksgiving always pleases God, and the Bible specifically calls on us to include thanksgiving when talking to God about those in authority.

We are to pray respectfully for leaders. "*Honor everyone. ... Fear God. Honor the emperor*" (1 Peter 2:17, ESV). We are to pray with the clear understanding that government authority is established by God. "*Let every person be subject to the governing authorities. For there is no authority except from God, and those that exist have been instituted by God*" (Romans 13:1, ESV). We also pray knowing that God's Word says, "*The king's heart is like channels of water in the hand of the Lord; He turns it wherever He wishes*" (Proverbs 21:1, NASB).

WHO TO PRAY FOR

Suggestion: Each day, pick one category and pray
for one or two individuals in that category.

President _____

Cabinet members _____

Senators _____

Congressional representatives _____

Supreme Court _____

Military leaders _____

Governor _____

State legislators _____

Mayor, police chief, sheriff _____

World leaders _____

Others _____

It is a great privilege, as well as our responsibility,
to pray for our government leaders.

—*Billy Graham*

WHAT TO PRAY FOR OUR LEADERS

One way to pray for leaders is to ask the Holy Spirit to stir up prayers from daily Bible reading. Let the words of a verse give you an idea of something important to pray that is appropriate for the specific leader you have in mind. Here are examples:

- Help [*name any leader*] to accept wise counsel. *Proverbs 11:14; 15:22*

- Open his/her heart to hear the Word of Truth and respond to the Gospel of salvation. *Ephesians 1:13*

- Teach [*name*] to trust in You. *Psalm 21:7*

- Guard [*name*] from the influence of the evil one. *2 Thessalonians 3:3*

- Give [*name*] discretion, wisdom, and understanding in making decisions. *1 Chronicles 22:12; 1 Kings 3:9*

- Open his/her heart to Your reproof and pour out Your Spirit on his/her leadership. *Proverbs 1:23*

- Deliver [*name*] from opinions contrary to Your Word. *Psalm 119:105*

- Protect [*name*] from harm, and bless and protect his/her family. *Psalm 21:11; Ezra 6:10*

- Enable [*name*] to carry out his/her duties with humility toward You and toward others. *1 Peter 5:5*

- Bless [*name*] with strength, endurance, and stamina. *1 Chronicles 16:11; Isaiah 40:31*

- Equip [*name*] to act according to Your will and to make choices pleasing to You. *Hebrews 13:20-21*

- Give [*name*] the courage to do the right thing even when urged to do the wrong thing. *Proverbs 2:11-15*

- Teach [*name*] to have a tender heart of compassion toward those he/she leads and serves. *Colossians 3:12*

I cried to Him with my mouth, and He was extolled
with my tongue. If I regard iniquity in my heart,
the Lord will not hear. But certainly

GOD HAS HEARD ME;

He has attended to the voice of my prayer. Blessed be God,
who has not turned away my prayer, nor His mercy from me!

—*Psalm 66:17-20*

DATE

DATE

Crying out to God, see page 29

Let me pour everything out to You, Lord.
Thank You for the knowledge that You hear me!
—*Billy Graham*

... That Christ may dwell in your hearts through faith; that you, being

ROOTED AND GROUNDED IN LOVE,

may be able to comprehend with all the saints what is the width
and length and depth and height—to know the love of Christ which
passes knowledge; that you may be filled with all the fullness of God.

—Ephesians 3:17-19

DATE

DATE

Jesus considered prayer more important than food, for the
Bible says that hours before breakfast, *"In the morning, having
risen a long while before daylight, He went out and departed to a
solitary place; and there He prayed"* (Mark 1:35).
—Billy Graham

Practical Advice From Billy Graham

Read thoughtfully and prayerfully, and then meditate on what you have read. Some people pride themselves on covering a set number of chapters each day—but have no idea what they have read when they are finished! In his helpful little booklet "Manna in the Morning," Dr. Stephen F. Olford wrote, "Read the portion at least three times. Read it carefully to discover what is there generally. The next time, peruse it for what is there specially. Then study it for what is there personally. ... [Then] say: 'Lord, as I look at this passage this morning, is there any command to obey? Is there any promise to claim? Is there any new thought to follow and pursue? Is there any sin to avoid? Is there any new thought about God? About the Lord Jesus? About the Holy Spirit? About the devil?' Seek to discover what God is saying to you from the passage you have read."

UNTO YOU I LIFT UP MY EYES, O You

who dwell in the heavens. Behold, as the eyes of servants look
to the hand of their masters, as the eyes of a maid to the hand
of her mistress, so our eyes look to the Lord our God,
until He has mercy on us.

—Psalm 123:1-2

DATE

DATE

God helps our praying, see page 6.

The reason many of the great saints have closed their eyes
while praying is to shut out the affairs of the world so that
their minds could be completely concentrated on their
conversations with God. However, nowhere in Scripture
does it say that even the closing of the eyes is important.
—*Billy Graham*

For as many as are led by the Spirit of God, these are sons of God.
For you did not receive the spirit of bondage again to fear, but you
received the Spirit of adoption by whom we cry out, "Abba, Father."
The Spirit Himself bears witness with our spirit that

WE ARE CHILDREN OF GOD.

—Romans 8:14–16

DATE

DATE

Waiting to hear from you, see page 63

Jesus said, *"When you pray, say: 'Our Father ...'"* (Luke 11:2). This
is a great comfort because God has a particular
responsibility to His children.
—*Billy Graham*

But **WHY DO YOU**
call Me "Lord, Lord," and not
do the things which I say?

—*Luke 6:46*

DATE

DATE

To Encourage You in Prayer

Pray Every Day

God wants to hear from you regularly. He wants a relationship. Take time to talk to God daily and throughout the day, not just when you face a crisis and not only with a list of wants and needs. *"Pray without ceasing"* (1 Thessalonians 5:17).

Dynamic prayer emanates from an obedient heart.
—*Billy Graham*

You did not choose Me, but **I CHOSE YOU**
and appointed you that you should go and bear fruit,
and that your fruit should remain, that whatever
you ask the Father in My name He may give you.

—John 15:16

DATE

DATE

"Yes" is not the only answer, see page 33

Every religion teaches that people ought to pray, but only
the Christian faith promises that God will answer.
—*Billy Graham*

IT IS CHRIST who died, and furthermore
is also risen, who is even at the right hand of God,
who also makes intercession for us.

Therefore He is also able to save to the uttermost those
who come to God through Him, since He always lives
to make intercession for them.

—Romans 8:34; Hebrews 7:25

DATE

DATE

Yearning for God, see page 39

Many may ask, "Is there no other way to pray except through Jesus Christ?" You may pray, but according to the Bible, *"There is ... one Mediator between God and men, the Man Christ Jesus"* (1 Timothy 2:5).
—*Billy Graham*

Pray for us. ... May the God of peace who brought up our
Lord Jesus from the dead, that great Shepherd of the sheep,
through the blood of the everlasting covenant,
MAKE YOU COMPLETE
in every good work to do His will, working in you what
is well pleasing in His sight, through Jesus Christ,
to whom be glory forever and ever. Amen.

—*Hebrews 13:18, 20-21*

DATE

DATE

Prayer couples you with God's true purposes for you and the world. It
not only brings the blessings of God's will to your own personal life,
but it brings you the added blessing of being in step with God's plan.
—*Billy Graham*

Creative Prayer Suggestion

Make a list of all the leaders in your church and their specific areas of ministry. Ask them for specific requests from time to time.

Therefore we also pray always for you that our God would count you worthy of this calling, and fulfill all the good pleasure of His goodness and the work of faith with power, that

THE NAME OF OUR LORD JESUS CHRIST MAY BE GLORIFIED

in you, and you in Him, according to the grace of our God and the Lord Jesus Christ.

—*2 Thessalonians 1:11–12*

DATE

DATE

When tempted to tell God how to answer, see page 45

Above all, be sure that your motive in praying is to glorify God. Our Lord said to His disciples, *"And whatsoever ye shall ask in my name, that will I do, that the Father may be glorified in the Son"* (John 14:13, KJV).
—Billy Graham

Therefore I exhort first of all that supplications,
prayers, intercessions, and giving of thanks
BE MADE FOR ALL MEN,
for kings and all who are in authority, that we may lead a quiet
and peaceable life in all godliness and reverence. For this is
good and acceptable in the sight of God our Savior.

—1 Timothy 2:1-3

DATE

DATE

Today's news, see page 76

Today the world is being carried on a rushing torrent of
history that is sweeping out of control. There is but one power
available to redeem the course of events, and that is the power
of prayer by God-fearing, Christ-believing men and women.
—*Billy Graham*

So it was, when I heard these words, that I sat down and wept, and mourned for many days; I was fasting and praying before the God of heaven. And I said: "I pray, Lord God of heaven, O great and awesome God, You who keep Your covenant and mercy with those who love You and observe Your commandments, please let Your ear be attentive and Your eyes open, that You may

HEAR THE PRAYER OF YOUR SERVANT

which I pray before You now, day and night.

—Nehemiah 1:4–6

DATE

DATE

Prayer that changes nations, see pages 36–37

Practical Advice From Billy Graham

Make prayer a central part of your time with God. In our Bible study, God speaks to us; in our prayer times, we speak to God. Make prayer first of all a time of praise and thanksgiving. Then pray about the passage of Scripture you have just read, asking Him to show you specific ways that it applies to your life. In addition, confess your sins to God. Finally, bring before God your own needs and the needs of others. Many people find it helpful to keep a prayer diary, in which they list those for whom they are praying and note God's specific answers.

DATE

DATE

From one end of the Bible to the other, there is the record
of those whose prayers have been answered—men and women
who turned the tide of history by prayer; men and women
who fervently prayed, and God answered.
—*Billy Graham*

Now to Him who is
ABLE TO DO EXCEEDINGLY ABUNDANTLY

above all that we ask or think, according to the power that
works in us, to Him be glory in the church by Christ Jesus
to all generations, forever and ever. Amen.

—Ephesians 3:20-21

DATE

DATE

Feeding your soul, see page 31

In this modern age in which we live, we have learned to harness
the power of the atom, but very few of us have learned how to
develop fully the power of prayer. We have not yet learned that
we are more powerful on our knees than behind the most
powerful weapons that can be developed.
—*Billy Graham*

Then He spoke a parable
to them, that men always ought to
PRAY and NOT LOSE HEART.
—Luke 18:1

DATE

DATE

God's delight in prayer, see page 49

How little perseverance and persistence and pleading we show.
Some time ago the newspapers told of a man in Washington
who spent 17 years securing favorable action on a claim of
$81,000 against the government. Yet many people will not
pray 17 minutes for the welfare of their own immortal
souls or the salvation of other people.

—*Billy Graham*

And this I pray, that your **LOVE MAY ABOUND** still more and more in knowledge and all discernment, that you may approve the things that are excellent, that you may be sincere and without offense till the day of Christ, being filled with the fruits of righteousness which are by Jesus Christ, to the glory and praise of God.

—*Philippians 1:9-11*

DATE

_____
_____
_____
_____
_____
_____
_____
_____
_____
_____
_____

DATE

_____
_____
_____
_____
_____

To Encourage You in Prayer

Pray for God's Glory

Pray for things to happen in such a way as to provide God with the credit and to give God the glory. He is powerful, magnificent, and majestic. And He is still our closest, most intimate Friend. Praise Him and ask for things that matter to Him. *"To God, alone wise, be glory through Jesus Christ forever. Amen"* (Romans 16:27).

A life taught in the Scriptures, and tuned in to God in
prayer, produces an outflowing of grace and power.
—*Billy Graham*

Peter PUT THEM ALL OUT,
and knelt down and prayed.
—Acts 9:40

DATE

DATE

God's own prayer request, see page 37

Our Lord frequently prayed alone, separating Himself
from every earthly distraction. I would strongly urge you
to select a room or corner in your home or in your yard
where you, alone, can regularly meet God.
—*Billy Graham*

But I say to you who hear: **LOVE YOUR ENEMIES,**
do good to those who hate you, bless those who curse you,
and pray for those who spitefully use you.

—*Luke 6:27-28*

DATE

DATE

Prayers that outlast you, see page 64

How startling His instructions and His example. He tells us to
pray for those who despitefully use you and persecute you.
In other words, He says to pray for your enemies. How many
of us have ever spent time praying for our enemies?
—*Billy Graham*

All things that the Father has are Mine. Therefore I said
that He will take of Mine and declare it to you. ...
Most assuredly, I say to you, whatever you

ASK THE FATHER IN MY NAME

He will give you. Until now you have asked nothing in My name.
Ask, and you will receive, that your joy may be full.

—John 16:15, 23-24

DATE

DATE

The Scripture says that the one Mediator between God and
us is Jesus Christ. You must know Him, and you must pray
in His Name. Your prayers must be directed according to
the will of God, and the Holy Spirit will do that for you.
—Billy Graham

DATE

Creative Prayer Suggestion

As you use this journal and read the suggested Scriptures, keep notes of the needs and people who come to mind and pray for them. Then, think of ways you could help answer each prayer need. For instance, who among your acquaintances needs a "cup of cold water" (see Matthew 10:42) from you today?

THE LORD IS NEAR to those who have
a broken heart, and saves such as have a contrite spirit.

Then [Jesus] opened His mouth and taught them, saying:
"Blessed are the poor in spirit, for theirs is the kingdom of heaven."

—*Psalm 34:18; Matthew 5:2-3*

DATE

DATE

Childlike prayer, see page 71

The mourning of inadequacy is a weeping that
catches the attention of God. The Bible says, *"The
Lord is nigh unto them that are of a broken heart; and saveth
such as be of a contrite spirit"* (Psalm 34:18, KJV).
—Billy Graham

[Abraham] DID NOT WAVER at the promise
of God through unbelief, but was strengthened in faith,
giving glory to God, and being fully convinced that what
He had promised He was also able to perform. And therefore
"it was accounted to him for righteousness."

—*Romans 4:20-22*

DATE

DATE

Prayers of faith answered, see page 36

Faith pleases God more than anything else. The Christian
life is dependent upon faith. We stand on faith; we live
on faith; we pray in faith. Faith is loved and honored
by God more than any other single thing.
—*Billy Graham*

"For MY THOUGHTS are not your thoughts,
nor are your ways My ways," says the Lord. ...
"I, the Lord, will hasten it in its time."

—Isaiah 55:8; 60:22

DATE

DATE

Practical Advice From Billy Graham

Put what you have learned into action, and walk with Christ every minute of the day. Perhaps God has been speaking to you in your quiet time about your relationship with someone in your family or a co-worker. Commit that situation into His hands—and then move forward in obedience and faith, knowing that the Holy Spirit will help you as you seek to have a right relationship with that person.

God knows what is best for us, and sometimes His answer to our prayers is "No" or "Not yet." But that shouldn't keep us from praying! God loves us, and He can be trusted to do what is best. The Bible tells us to *"pray without ceasing"* (1 Thessalonians 5:17).
—*Billy Graham*

... Praying always with all prayer and supplication

IN THE SPIRIT,

being watchful to this end with all perseverance
and supplication for all the saints—and for me ...

—*Ephesians 6:18-19*

DATE

DATE

Praying for God's own desire, see page 37

That *"the Spirit Himself makes intercession"* (Romans 8:26)
indicates that it is actually God pleading, praying, and mourning
through us. Thus we become co-laborers with God, actual partners
with Him (see 2 Corinthians 6:1); our lives are lifted from the low
plane of selfishness to the high plane of creativeness with God.
—*Billy Graham*

Then [Jesus] said to them, "Nation will rise against nation, and kingdom against kingdom. And there will be great earthquakes in various places, and famines and pestilences; and there will be fearful sights and great signs from heaven. ...
Now when these things begin to happen,

LOOK UP AND LIFT UP YOUR HEADS,

because your redemption draws near."

—Luke 21:10-11, 28

DATE

DATE

A powerful way to pray God's Word, see page 65

In the middle of our world troubles, the Christian is not to go about
wringing his hands, shouting: "What shall we do?" and having more
nervous tension and worry than anyone else. The Christian is to trust
quietly that God is still on the throne. He is a Sovereign God,
working out things according to His own plan.

—*Billy Graham*

Search me, O God, and KNOW MY HEART;
try me, and know my anxieties; and see if there is any
wicked way in me, and lead me in the way everlasting.

—Psalm 139:23-24

DATE

DATE

Get on your knees before God and ask Him if there are any areas
of your life that are still unyielded to Him. The searchlight of His
Spirit will probe the inner depths of your soul and reveal things
that you think you have already yielded, but you have not.
—Billy Graham

Creative Prayer Suggestion

Review "Praying for the Nations" on page 37. Use those suggestions to pick several countries and have your family find out more about them. Using sources such as *National Geographic,* do a pictorial display in a scrapbook or on a bulletin board and use that as a focal point for prayer.

Do not remember the former things,
nor consider the things of old.
BEHOLD, I WILL DO A NEW THING,
now it shall spring forth; shall you not know it?

—*Isaiah 43:18-19*

DATE

DATE

How to delight God, see page 35

You were created in the image and likeness of God. You were made
for God's fellowship and your heart can never be satisfied without
His communion. Let your prayer be like that of the psalmist, "O God,
You are my God; early will I seek You; my soul thirsts for You; my flesh longs
for You in a dry and thirsty land where there is no water" (Psalm 63:1).
—Billy Graham

131

But as many as received Him,
TO THEM HE GAVE THE RIGHT
to become children of God, to those who believe in His name.

—John 1:12

DATE _____

_____
_____
_____
_____
_____
_____
_____
_____
_____

DATE _____

_____
_____
_____
_____
_____
_____
_____
_____
_____

Practical advice on prayer, see page 7

I have had new Christians say to me, "I don't know how to pray. I don't have the right words." When our children were just learning to talk and had difficulty finding the right words, they still managed to make themselves understood to my wife and me, and the mistakes they made only endeared them to us. In fact, I am sure I treasure their early attempts at conversation more than the words of most adults speaking without hesitation and without error.

—*Billy Graham*

You ask and do not receive,

BECAUSE YOU ASK WRONGLY,

to spend it on your passions.

—James 4:3, ESV

DATE _____

_____
_____
_____
_____
_____
_____
_____
_____
_____
_____

DATE _____

_____
_____
_____
_____
_____
_____
_____
_____
_____
_____

Creative Prayer Suggestion

Get a list of all missionaries and organizations your church supports. Many have monthly newsletters that keep you informed so you can pray more specifically. Perhaps pray for one or two missionaries or organizations each month.

Prayer serves a dual purpose: the blessing of man and the glory of God. If a prayer is prayed willfully for our own benefit but not for God's glory, it's not worthy of being answered. *"Not my will, but Yours, be done"* (Luke 22:42) is the spirit of effectual prayer.

—*Billy Graham*

The Lord is near
TO ALL WHO CALL ON HIM,
to all who call on him in truth.

—Psalm 145:18, ESV

DATE

DATE

Removing an impediment to prayer, see page 47

DATE

As a young man, I wrote to my mother, "I know that I
know Jesus Christ, but I've lost my feeling. I can't seem to get
anywhere in prayer. I don't feel anything." "Son, God is testing
you," she wrote back. "He tells us to walk not by feeling but by
faith, and when you don't feel anything, God may be closer to you
than ever before. Through the darkness and through the fog, put
your hand up by faith. You'll sense the touch of God."
—*Billy Graham*

I desire therefore that the men PRAY EVERYWHERE,
lifting up holy hands, without wrath and doubting.

—*1 Timothy 2:8*

DATE

DATE

Praying for someone you don't know, see page 41

A question many ask is: "Who is told to pray?" Scripture gives the answer, "All men." Again, many ask: "Where are we commanded to pray?" Paul gives us the answer when he says, "Everywhere." Some may also ask, "When are we told to pray?" The Scripture says, "Always." It is a command, a duty, and a privilege.

—Billy Graham

139

While they were worshiping the Lord and fasting, the Holy Spirit said, "Set apart for me Barnabas and Saul for the work to which I have called them." Then after

FASTING AND PRAYING

they laid their hands on them and sent them off.

—Acts 13:2-3, ESV

DATE

DATE

God's own prayer request, see page 37

Scores of missionaries, in all parts of the world, have told me,
"Please get the people back home to pray for us. We would rather
have their prayers than anything else." If the Christians back home
realized how much their prayers meant to these valiant heroes
of the faith, they would not cease to pray day and night for their
representatives out there in foreign mission fields.

—*Billy Graham*

CONTINUE STEADFASTLY in prayer,
being watchful in it with thanksgiving.

—*Colossians 4:2, ESV*

DATE

DATE

Praying for a loved one who needs the Savior, see page 22

When you pray, your physical posture is not so important as the attitude of your heart. Many people put a great deal of emphasis on the position of the body during prayer. Some groups or sects insist that you kneel every time you pray or that you fold your hands in a certain way. All of this is relatively unimportant, though kneeling is an act of humility when sincerely done.

—*Billy Graham*

143

PRAY WITHOUT CEASING.

—1 Thessalonians 5:17

DATE

DATE

When you don't know how to pray, see page 133

We are to pray in times of adversity, lest we become faithless
and unbelieving. We are to pray in times of prosperity, lest we
become boastful and proud. We are to pray in times of danger,
lest we become fearful and doubting. We need to pray in times
of security, lest we become self-sufficient.

—*Billy Graham*

Seeing then that we have a GREAT HIGH PRIEST
who has passed through the heavens, Jesus the Son of God ...
let us therefore come boldly to the throne of grace.

—*Hebrews 4:14, 16*

DATE

DATE

Praying for people in need, see pages 54 and 117

God, for Christ's sake, forgives our sins. God, for Christ's sake, supplies our needs. God, for Christ's sake, receives our prayers. The person who comes with confidence to the throne of grace has seen that his approach to God has been made possible because of Jesus Christ.

—*Billy Graham*

Now it came to pass in those days that
He went out to the mountain to pray, and
CONTINUED ALL NIGHT
in prayer to God.

—Luke 6:12

DATE

DATE

What pleases God, see page 121

The precious hours of fellowship with His Heavenly Father
meant more to our Savior than sleep.

—*Billy Graham*

[Jesus said,] "Father, if it is YOUR WILL,
take this cup away from Me; nevertheless
not My will, but Yours, be done."

—*Luke 22:42*

DATE

DATE

Unexpected answers to delight you, see page 26

We must desire the will of God. Even our Lord, contrary to
His own disposition at the moment, said, *"O My Father, if this cup
cannot pass away from Me ... , Your will be done"* (Matthew 26:42).

—*Billy Graham*

Who shall separate us from the love of Christ?
Shall tribulation, or distress, or persecution, or famine,
or nakedness, or danger, or sword? ... No, in all these things

WE ARE MORE THAN CONQUERORS

through him who loved us.

—*Romans 8:35, 37, ESV*

DATE

DATE

God Himself prays with you, see page 125

As the hymn says, "Satan trembles when he sees the
weakest saint upon his knees"—so pray, Christian, pray!

—*Billy Graham*

SOURCES

"Prayer," by Billy Graham, is excerpted and updated from a sermon classic ©1955 (renewed 1983, revised 1993, 1994, 2001, 2005, 2006) Billy Graham Evangelistic Association.

Quotations on pages 19, 40, 61, 87, 105 (top), and 122 are from "Have a Vital Time Alone With God," presented by Billy Graham at a conference in Amsterdam, The Netherlands, July 1983, and published in *A Biblical Standard for Evangelists* ©1984 Billy Graham Evangelistic Association.

"A Powerful Way to Pray God's Word," by Robert J. Morgan, was originally published in *Christian Reader* magazine, July 1999, under the title "What Ruth Graham Taught Me About Prayer: A powerful way to make God's words your own" ©Robert J. Morgan, used by permission.

Quotations on pages 4, 21, 22, 25, 33, 35, 41, 43, 45, 49, 53, 55, 57, 59, 64, 69, 70, 77, 80, and 123 are from Billy Graham's *My Answer* syndicated newspaper columns, various dates, used by permission.

Quotations from Billy Graham on pages 17, 18, 29, 86, 89, 91, 93, 95, 97, 98, 101, 103, 105, 107, 109, 113, 115, 116, 127, 128, 133-135, and 139-153 are from Billy Graham sermon collections, various dates, ©Billy Graham Evangelistic Association.

Quotations on pages 15, 31, 39, 73, 75, 79, 85, 119, 121, 125, and 131 are from *Day by Day with Billy Graham*, by Billy Graham, ©1976 Billy Graham Evangelistic Association.

Quotations on pages 27 and 111 are from *A Biblical Standard for Evangelists*, by Billy Graham ©1984 Billy Graham Evangelistic Association.

Quotation on page 137 is from *Just As I Am*, by Billy Graham ©1997 Billy Graham Evangelistic Association.

Page 23 is excerpted from a letter from Billy Graham dated February 20, 2013.

Quotation at top of page 37 is from a letter from Billy Graham dated November 2011.

Quotations on pages 40, 60, 63, and back cover are from public comments by Billy Graham. (The quotation on back cover alludes to a statement that originated with Cameron V. Thompson.)